FRIEDRICH KUHLAU
(1786-1832)

SONATINAS, OP. 20 AND
SONATINAS, OP. 55 FOR THE PIANO
Edited by Keith Snell

D1302420

CONTENTS

For supplementary study, a compact disc recording of the Sonatinas Op. 20 *and* Sonatinas Op. 55 *is available from your favorite music dealer (WP394CD), Nelita True, piano. Ms. True's interpretations follow this edition closely as a practical example for students.*

ISBN 0-8497-9616-4

FRIEDRICH KUHLAU (1786-1832)

Friedrich Kuhlau (1786-1832) was born in Hanover, Germany. While he was still very young, he moved with his parents to Hamburg, Germany. There he studied music with Friedrich Gottlieb Schwenke. Schwenke had been a student of the well known composer Johann Philip Kirnberger. Kirnberger had been a student of the great Johann Sebastian Bach. Therefore, Kuhlau could tout his musical heritage to J. S. Bach.

Kuhlau was highly regarded as a musician in Hamburg. He earned an excellent reputation as a piano teacher and in 1808 he gave a successful debut recital in Hamburg. Soon after he began publishing his own piano music.

In 1810, Kuhlau moved to Copenhagen, Denmark when Hamburg was annexed to the French Empire. He lived there for the rest of his life. In 1813 he was appointed a member of the Royal Orchestra of the King's Court where he played flute as well as piano. He became known as the "Great Danish Composer" for his restoration of the National Opera when he composed several very successful operas which used popular national songs. In 1825, Kuhlau gained the respect and friendship of Ludwig van Beethoven during a visit to Vienna. It was on this occasion that Beethoven wrote the famed humorous canon on Kuhlau name, *"Kuhl, nicht lau,"* -cool, not lukewarm!

Kuhlau's most enduring contribution is the wealth of original repertoire for the flute and collections of sonatas and sonatinas for the piano. The *Sonatinas Op. 20* and *Op. 55* are some of the most delightful pieces from the classical period for intermediate levels. The study of these sonatinas provides an excellent preparation for playing more advanced piano sonatas of this period.

Sonatina Form

A SONATINA is a short sonata. Sonatinas provide excellent music to play before studying longer, more complicated sonatas. Many first movements are based on a form called *sonata-allegro*, which was commonly used during the classical period of music writing (1770-1820).

A sonatina or sonata may have one, two or three movements. If there is more than one movement, they are usually contrasting in tempo and character.

First movements usually have this form *(sonata-allegro)*:
1. EXPOSITION
   - a) first theme
   - b) second theme (usually in a contrasting key)
   - c) closing theme (optional)

2. DEVELOPMENT
   Themes are presented in new keys and sometimes new material is added.

3. RECAPITULATION
   - a) first theme
   - b) second theme
   - c) closing theme (optional)

Second movements are usually written in three parts, or *ternary form* (ABA)
   - A. first theme
   - B. second theme
   - A. first theme

Third movements are often written in *rondo* form:
   - A. first theme
   - B. second theme
   - C. third theme
   - A. first theme
   - B. second theme
   - Coda (optional)

Sonatina in C major
Opus 20, No. 1

Rondo
Allegro

Sonatina in G major

Opus 20, No. 2

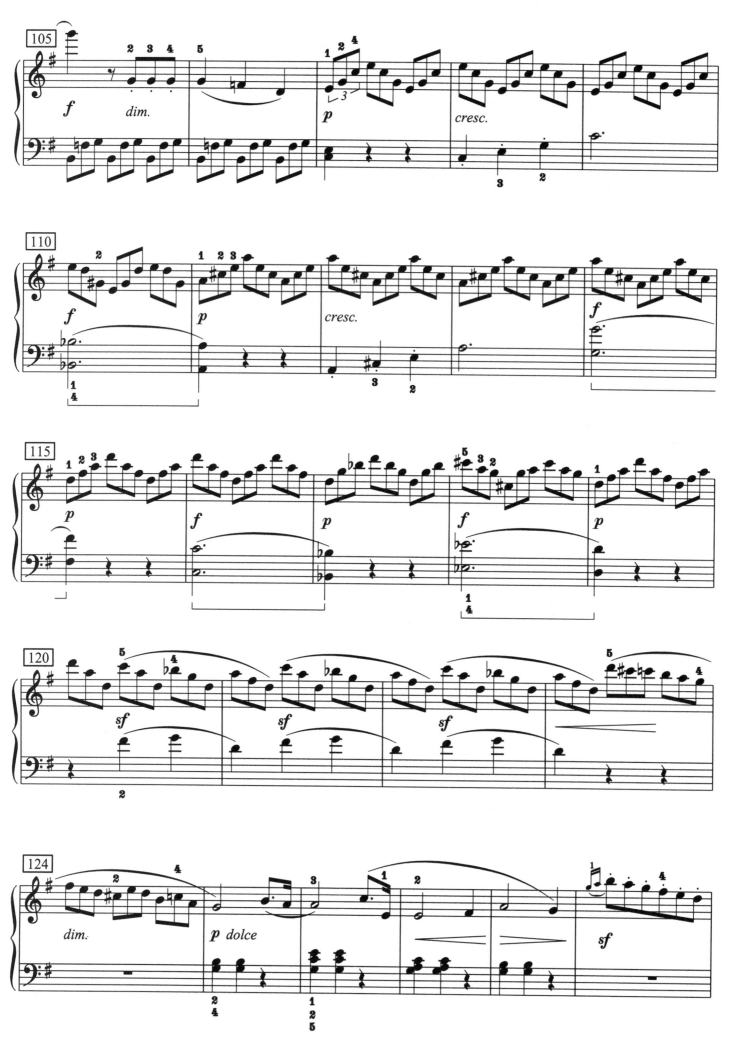

SONATINA IN F MAJOR

Opus 20, No. 3

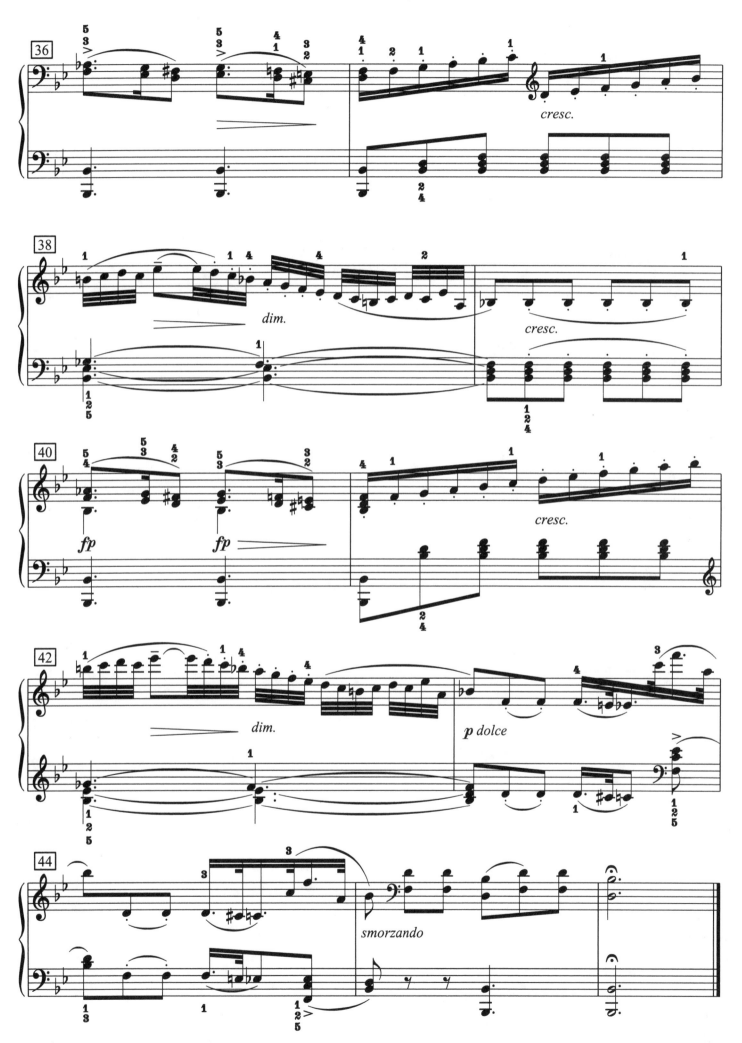

Alla Polacca

SONATINA IN C MAJOR

Opus 55, No. 1

Rondo

SONATINA IN G MAJOR
Opus 55, No. 3

Sonatina in C Major

Opus 55, No. 3

Allegro con spirito

Allegretto grazioso

SONATINA IN F MAJOR
Opus 55, No. 4

Andantino con espressione

Alla polacca

Da capo al segno 𝄋, e poi la Coda

SONATINA IN D MAJOR

Opus 55, No. 5

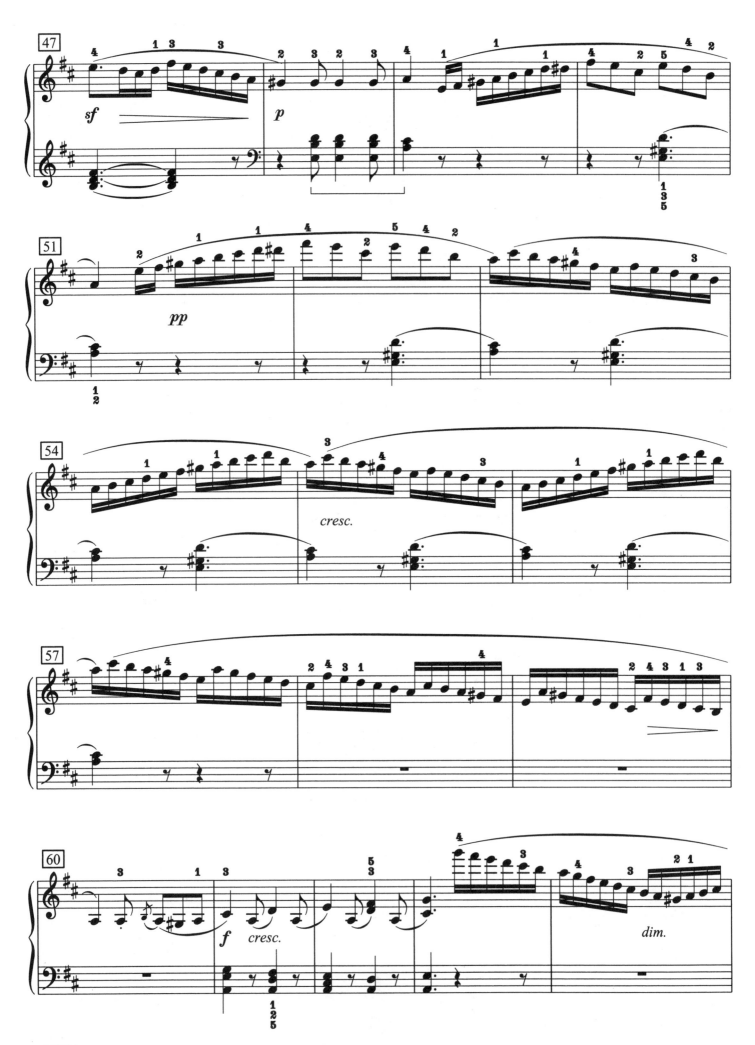

SONATINA IN C MAJOR

Opus 55, No. 6

Menuetto

Menuetto da Capo senza replica, e poi la Coda